The Foster Carer's Handbook on Health

GETTING THE BEST FOR YOUR CHILD

Hannah Smith and
Nikki Shepherd

Published by
CoramBAAF Adoption and Fostering Academy
41 Brunswick Square
London WC1N 1AZ
www.corambaaf.org.uk

Coram Academy Limited, registered as a company limited by guarantee
in England and Wales number 9697712, part of the Coram group,
charity number 312278

British Library Cataloguing in Publication Data
A catalogue record for this book is available from the British Library

ISBN 978 1 910039 95 3

Project management by Jo Francis, CoramBAAF
Designed and typeset by Helen Joubert Designs
Printed in Great Britain by The Lavenham Press

Trade distribution by Turnaround Publisher Services, Unit 3, Olympia
Trading Estate, Coburg Road, London N22 6TZ

 For the latest news on CoramBAAF titles and special offers, sign up to our
free publications bulletin at https://corambaaf.org.uk/subscribe.

Contents

Acknowledgements

The authors would like to thank CoramBAAF for the opportunity to be involved in writing this guidance book for foster carers. The health of looked after children has been a passion for both authors for many years and it is hoped that this book will help to support foster carers to succeed in their roles as advocates and positive role models for the health and well-being of all looked after children.

About the authors

Hannah Smith (RN, Specialist Public Health Nursing HV), worked as a Designated Nurse for Looked after Children in Calderdale until her retirement from the NHS in 2018. She was recently appointed by West Yorkshire Police as a Case Conference Officer in a district Safeguarding Unit. Her passion for championing the health needs of children in care remains strong, and she continues to sit on fostering panels as an independent panel member in the independent sector, as well as being a Special Adviser for children's safeguarding with the Care Quality Commission.

Nikki Shepherd (RN, BMedSci, MA, PG in Healthcare Leadership) has worked as a Designated Nurse for Looked after Children since 2005 in the provider service, and from 2015 in Sheffield CCG and, more recently, Barnsley CCG. Previously, she worked as a specialist nurse for looked after children in residential homes for a number of years. She is a panel Chair for a local authority fostering panel and also sits as an independent panel member in the independent sector.

Foreword

This book has been written to guide and support newly approved foster carers and connected carers who have entered into this role to make a difference to some of the most vulnerable children in our society. Established foster carers and connected carers may also find useful information here. As health professionals, the authors recognise the fundamental importance of good physical and mental health to support any possibility of improving a child's life chances and outcomes, and this guide is a starting point for all newly approved foster carers to negotiate what can at times seem a convoluted health system to get the services that a child in care needs.

It is recognised by the authors that fostering is a tough job; on a daily basis, foster carers are expected to problem-solve, organise, support and comfort children who, for a variety of reasons, display behaviours and challenges that can test a carer's patience, resilience and stamina to the limit. However, the authors know from many years' experience of working alongside carers that the rewards and achievements gained through fostering, even if these involve only small improvements to a child's behaviour, will often eclipse the tough times.

The authors acknowledge that during the final stages of writing this book, the COVID-19 pandemic resulted in a national period of "lockdown". This in turn impacted on looked after children's ability to access their education and enforced a period of social isolation within fostering households and residential homes. The impact this will have had on increasing levels of feelings of isolation and emotional distress should not be underestimated. Foster carers, once again, have had a unique role to play in supporting looked after children through what has been an unprecedented period in all our lives.

1 Introduction

"Looked after child" is a generic term introduced in the Children Act 1989 to describe children and young people subject to care orders (placed into the care of a local authority by order of a court) and children accommodated under section 20 (voluntary agreement by parents to have the child taken into care) of the Children Act 1989.

There are a variety of care settings for looked after children: they may live in foster homes, residential units, with family members (often called connected carers, or kinship carers), or in some cases with their own parents on a care order.

Under the Children Act 1989, a child is legally defined as "looked after" by a local authority if they:

- are provided with accommodation continuously for a period of 24 hours;
- are subject to a care order; or
- are subject to a placement order.

This book is designed to assist newly approved foster carers to navigate their way through health service provision in order to ensure that looked after children's health needs are met and to improve their long-term health outcomes. Established foster carers may also find the content of this guide useful, as learning and development in the role of foster care is limitless.

Foster carers have a fundamental role in identifying children's health problems and issues that have not been previously addressed, as well as supporting children with already identified health needs. Health can be defined as physical, emotional and social health, which are inter-dependent on each other, like a balancing act – in order to attain best outcomes for children and young people, they will need to have all aspects of their health functioning at an optimum.

Foster carers are one of the most important resources for children in the care system, and this is why a section of this book focuses on the health and well-being of carers. As a foster carer, you will be an important influence and role model for the children and young people in your care. Fostering households should promote a healthy lifestyle and lead by example; the long-term benefits of this would be to improve outcomes for everyone living in the fostering home.

Foster carers should never feel like they are working in isolation, as there is a whole team of professionals available to support and advise them. Communication and working in partnership are the keys to success. The diagram below identifies some important professionals who are an excellent source of support and advice for foster carers. Your social worker should be able to provide you with information about the professional team and their contribution to the child/children in your care.

The team around the foster carer

The health needs of looked after children

Evidence from research shows that looked after children and young people share many of the same health risks and problems as their peers, but often to a greater degree. Children frequently enter the care system with poorer health than other children, in part due to the impact of poverty, poor parenting, chaotic lifestyles and abuse or neglect. The longer term outcomes for looked after children remain worse than those for their non-looked after peers, and upon leaving care, young people are known to experience additional detrimental health outcomes (Department for Education and Department of Health, 2015).

Children and young people in care may also have specific medical conditions and needs or disabilities, whereas others may need help with mental health issues and emotional health. The continuity of children's health care may be impaired due to their frequent moves within the care system, and this can be compounded by their medical history and other important information being delayed in transfer or lost.

Below is a list of five common children's health needs identified at the initial health assessment:

- immunisations (not fully immunised);

- dental issues;

- speech and language delay;

- emotional health issues;

- associated health needs as a result of premature birth.

This list is reflective of the national reporting on health issues, as found in the Department for Education document, *A Guide to Looked After Children Statistics in England* (2019, version 1.4). For children who are looked after in Wales, Scotland or Northern Ireland, the websites listed below can provide similar information:

- https://statswales.gov.wales

- www.gov.scot

- www.health-ni.gov.uk

The landscape of the NHS

Understanding the way in which the NHS is structured will help you, as a foster carer, to know where to turn for health support for the children you are looking after.

The NHS was established on 5 July 1948 as a health service, free at the point of contact for all residents in England regardless of wealth. It was structured into three tiers:

- hospitals;
- family doctors, dentists, opticians and pharmacists;
- local authority health services (community care, school health services and maternity care).

Over subsequent years, the organisation of the NHS has evolved and the service of today is a more complex organisation for patients to navigate their way around. Simply put, due to the introduction of the Health and Social Care Act 2012, today's NHS now consists of:

- The Department of Health (DH), which has the overarching responsibility for funding and policy development across the UK;
- NHS England, which is an independent organisation that oversees healthcare commissioning and provision (commissioning means deciding on, arranging and purchasing);
- Clinical Commissioning Groups (CCGs), which are clinically-led statutory NHS bodies responsible for planning and commissioning healthcare for a local area;
- NHS Foundation Trusts, which are often referred to as "provider" services, providing the care that the CCGs commission. They include hospitals, ambulance, mental health, and primary care services.

The NHS structure can be complicated and at times may be overwhelming when carers are trying to find a service for a child. Your local looked after children's health team is a good source of support when identifying appropriate services for the child in your care.

It is recognised that NHS structures and legislation for Scotland, Northern Ireland and Wales may differ.

Scotland

Responsibility for the National Health Services in Scotland is a devolved matter and rests with the Scottish Government. Legislation about the NHS is made by the Scottish Parliament. The Scottish Government sets national objectives and priorities for the NHS, monitors performance, and supports Boards to ensure achievement of these key objectives. NHS Boards in Scotland are all-purpose organisations: they plan, commission and deliver NHS services and take overall responsibility for the health of their populations. They therefore plan and commission hospital and community health services, including services provided by GPs, dentists, community pharmacists and opticians, who are independent contractors.

Northern Ireland

In Northern Ireland, the NHS is referred to as HSC or Health and Social Care. Just like the NHS, it is free at the point of contact, but in Northern Ireland it also provides social care services like home care, family and children's services, day care and social work. The Department of Health, Social Services and Public Safety (DHSSPS) has authority for health and social care services. Services are commissioned by the Health and Social Care Board (HSCB) and provided by five Health and Social Care Trusts. The HSCB, which sits between the Department and Trusts, is responsible for commissioning services, managing resources and performance improvement. The HSCB is also directly responsible for managing contracts for family health services provided by GPs, dentists, opticians and community pharmacists. These are all services not provided by Health and Social Care Trusts.

Wales

The reorganisation of NHS Wales, from 1 October 2009, created single local health organisations that are responsible for delivering all healthcare services within a geographical area, rather than the Trust and Local Health Board system that existed previously. The NHS now delivers services through seven Health Boards and three NHS Trusts in Wales.

Accessing universal services

The term "universal services" in relation to health care incorporates services provided by GP practices, dentists, opticians, health visitors and school nurses (now known as 0–19 services). All children are entitled to receive universal health care services, and foster carers are expected to ensure that looked after children in their care access these services.

Registering with a GP

GP practices must accept registration of a patient, unless there are reasonable grounds to refuse.

Since January 2015, all GP practices in England have been free to register new patients who live outside their practice boundary area. It is for a GP practice to decide at the point of registration whether it is clinically appropriate and practical to register individual patients.

Foster carers will need to formally register a child in their care with a GP practice by completing and submitting a registration form, and this should be done as a priority.

Some GP practices may ask for proof of identity of the child you are registering; however, they cannot refuse to register the child if you do not have documents to hand. It is advisable to introduce yourself to the practice manager as a newly approved foster carer, before the need to register a child arises, therefore avoiding unnecessary delay.

It is important to register the child/young person as a "permanent registration" so that the child's full records are sent to the practice. The GP will have to ask for the records to be fast-tracked as this does not automatically happen.

The above process also applies to patients who are categorised as asylum-seekers, refugees, homeless or overseas visitors, whether they are in the UK lawfully or not.

For further information, visit:

- www.nhs.uk
- www.nhsdirect.wales.nhs.uk

- www.nidirect.gov.uk
- www.nhsinform.scot

Registering with a dentist

There is no need to register with a dentist in the same way as with a GP because you are not bound to a catchment area (that is, you do not have to go to a dentist near to where you live). It may be that the child in your care is already registered with a dentist, and if the practice is within a reasonable distance from your home, it is advisable that the child continues attending at their registered practice. Just remember to update contact details with the dental practice.

If the child is not registered with a dentist, simply find a dental practice that is convenient for you, and contact them to see if there are any appointments available.

You can search for an NHS dentist by visiting:

- www.nhs.uk
- www.nhsdirect.wales.nhs.uk
- www.nidirect.gov.uk
- www.nhsinform.scot

Problems finding an NHS dentist?

If you are having difficulty finding a dentist accepting NHS patients in England, you should call NHS England's Customer Contact Centre on 0300 311 2233. NHS England commissions dental services across England and is required to ensure that there are enough dental services in an area to meet the needs of the local population for both urgent and routine dental care.

Should you encounter any further problems finding a dentist, you should contact your local looked after children's health team or the Designated Nurse for looked after children in your area, for advice and support.

Registering with an optician

Regular vision checks are important for all children, as changes in vision can occur very quickly.

Many looked after children will not have had any vision screening or testing, so alongside registering with a GP and dentist, one of your first tasks as a foster carer is to find an optician and arrange an appointment for the child in your care.

As with dental registration, you are not bound to a catchment area. It may be that the child is already receiving care from an optician, and if this is the case and the child's optician is within a reasonable distance from your home, it is advisable that the child continues to attend there; just remember to update contact details at the optician.

The Association of Optometrists and the Federation of Ophthalmic and Dispensing Opticians have agreed the minimal intervals between sight tests, depending on the age of the patient and any pre-existing clinical conditions. For children, this means eyesight should be tested:

- For under 16 years in the absence of any binocular vision anomaly:[1] annually.

- For under 7 years with binocular vision anomaly or corrected refractive error:[2] six-monthly.

- For 7 years and over and under-16 with binocular vision anomaly or rapidly progressing myopia:[3] six-monthly.

- For 16 years and over, and under 70 years: every two years.

- Diabetic patients: annually.

---

1   Medical condition when the two eyes do not work well together, often causing headaches or eye strain.

2   Medical condition where there is a problem with the way the eye focuses. It is corrected with glasses or contact lenses.

3   Also known as short-sightedness, when objects can be seen clearly when close, but are blurred at a distance.

2 The importance of statutory health assessments

There are various statutory duties for health assessments of looked after children in the different UK countries, but the regulations throughout the UK require the local authority to ensure that the child has a comprehensive initial health assessment prior to or shortly after placement (unless an assessment has already been carried out in the last three months).

Initial health assessment

In England and Northern Ireland, the initial health assessment (IHA) must be carried out by a registered medical practitioner. In Wales, it is completed by a registered nurse with the appropriate knowledge and skills, or a paediatrician may complete it for children aged under five. In Scotland, it can be carried out by either a registered medical practitioner or a registered nurse.

- The Children Act 1989 and England's statutory guidance on *Promoting the Health and Wellbeing of Looked after Children* (DfE and DH, 2015) set out the requirements and timings for statutory health assessments for looked after children.

- In Scotland, *Guidance on Health Assessments for Looked After Children in Scotland* (Scottish Government, 2014) sets out the requirements, including around assessments and timings.

- In Wales, the guidance *Towards a Stable Life and a Brighter Future* (Welsh Assembly Government, 2007) sets out the requirements for assessments and when these should be done.

As stated, it is the responsibility of the looked after child's local authority to ensure that statutory health assessments are carried out. This can only happen with consent from the person/s with parental responsibility for the child.

Generally, an initial health assessment should be undertaken soon after a child enters care, unless an assessment has already been carried out in the last three months. In England, the first health assessment is called an Initial Health Assessment (IHA), and must take place within 20 working days of a child entering care; this should in theory coincide with the first statutory review by the Independent Reviewing Officer (IRO). The majority of health teams undertaking these assessments use CoramBAAF assessment forms, which follow a standardised screening pathway. For differences in approach between the UK countries, see the guidance noted in the bullet points above.

The initial health assessment is a holistic health assessment and screening opportunity, undertaken by a medical practitioner, usually a paediatrician in the specialist looked after children's health team. This may vary depending on the area you live in; the assessment may also be undertaken by a GP.

The child's social worker will liaise with the local looked after children's health team and arrange the initial health assessment appointment. It is essential that foster carers prioritise the appointment and make every effort to attend in order to ensure that any identified pre-care health issues and any ongoing health issues that may affect the child or young person can be addressed.

For many children, entering care is often the first time that they will have had any health screening, and given the higher levels of neglect around health issues experienced by looked after children, it is very important to make sure the child attends the appointment. For many children, this can be an anxious time, and foster carers will need to reassure the child in their care that this is not a medical examination in a hospital; it is a screening assessment that involves a conversation with a doctor to see if they are healthy and growing as they should be.

Screening looks at a variety of health indicators, such as:

- immunisation status;
- dental health;
- vision;
- development;
- emotional health and well-being;
- blood-borne viruses (BBV);

- genetic and hereditary conditions.

Additionally, for older children and young people, screening is important to identify lifestyle issues, such as:

- alcohol and substance misuse;

- sexual health and contraception.

Although screening and assessment is led by a medical professional, it must be emphasised that it is not necessarily a physical examination, and therefore it is unlikely that an older child will be asked to get undressed at the appointment; this will only be the case if clinically indicated. In most cases, where it is identified that a child needs a blood test or immunisation, it is unlikely that this will be undertaken at the assessment; usually a referral back to the GP or hospital is arranged. It may be useful to contact the team undertaking the assessment to check out local arrangements, and to be sure to give reassurance to the child or young person in your care about the process and what it entails. Remember, this can be a frightening prospect for some children, and it is known from research that looked after children and young people have higher levels of anxiety about their health than their peers (Bazalgette *et al*, 2015).

Prior to attending the initial health assessment, you may be asked, as a foster carer, to complete the CoramBAAF carer's report, which gives the assessing doctor essential health information about the child and, from your perspective, an overview, albeit from a brief period of time, as to what the child is like to care for. It is accepted that this information may be limited due to the fact that you may have had the child in your care for only a week or two before the assessment. However, any additional information that you can provide will be helpful to include.

It is considered good practice that the child's birth parent/s are invited to attend the initial health assessment (if appropriate), and the social worker should make every effort to encourage and support them to attend. This is an opportunity for health professionals to gain important information about birth parents' own health and whether any of their health issues could potentially impact on the health of their child, for example, genetic conditions, hereditary health conditions and lifestyle choices during pregnancy. For instance, a birth mother disclosing intravenous drug use should alert the medical practitioner to the possible need to screen the child for blood-borne viruses such as Hepatitis C or HIV.

At the end of the assessment, the doctor will develop a **health plan** that they will discuss with you, and you, along with the child's social worker, will be provided with a copy for your records.

The health plan will identify any unmet health needs and actions that will need to be taken to address these, as well as identifying who is responsible for progressing the plan. It may well be that as the child's foster carer, you are responsible for some actions, for example, taking a child to the dentist; whereas some interventions and actions may require referral to specialist health services such as speech and language therapy. The assessing doctor will identify who is responsible for such referrals and document this on the plan.

The health assessment and plan will be added to the relevant local authority care system record, and will form part of the child's care plan. This in turn will be monitored and reviewed by the child's social worker and the IRO at subsequent statutory looked after children (LAC) reviews. The plan should always be discussed at the child's statutory review, to ensure that progress against it is being made.

Health assessments are not isolated events. Information gained at the initial health assessment should be continuously reviewed and monitored by all who are responsible for the care of the child, and action on health issues should be taken by the due date set. This is to ensure that drift does not set in, and in the case of a child moving placement before the actions have been completed, it is very important that there is a clear handover of any outstanding actions on the health plan, particularly if these tasks are now to be undertaken by the new foster carers.

Review health assessment

Following on from the initial health assessment is the review health assessment (RHA), which takes place every six months for a child aged under five and annually for children aged over five for as long as they remain in the care system. This assessment is usually undertaken by a nurse, such as the specialist looked after children's nurse, or a health professional from the 0–19 service, depending on how health services have been set up in your area.

The format for the review health assessment is very similar to that for the initial health assessment and is again a screening opportunity. The assessment seeks the views of the child on their own health needs, if they are at an appropriate age to be able to contribute to the assessment. It culminates with a new health plan, which again is part of the child's overall care plan held by the local authority, is monitored by the child's social worker, and is reviewed by the IRO at subsequent statutory looked after children (LAC) reviews.

Whilst the initial health assessment is likely to be in a clinic-based setting, the review health assessment usually takes place away from a clinic environment and, dependent on the child's age, at a place where the child or young person feels comfortable. This could be at the child's foster home, at school, at a café or at a play gym.

In our experience of leading looked after children's health teams, the statutory health assessment process shows that the robust monitoring of the health needs of children in care will address unmet health needs. This will ultimately result in children being able to meet their full potential in relation to health, as well as having improved long-term outcomes in relation to their physical and mental health.

As a foster carer, you are key to helping with this process, and your input and engagement are essential.

Top tips for child health assessment

Before the assessment

- Prioritise the health assessment appointment.
- Check date, time and venue.
- Notify the child's social worker of the appointment.
- Are birth parents attending? (This will be decided by the social worker.)
- Complete the carer's report, take it with you.
- If you have the child's red book (health record), bring it with you.
- Check out local health team arrangements and likely waiting time.
- Who's doing the assessment?
- Will there be bloods taken or immunisations?

Inform the child

- Prepare your child or young person by explaining the health assessment process.

- If birth parents are attending, prepare the child in advance by letting them know they will be there.

- Positively promote this assessment – it's a good thing!

- Reassurance, it can be a bit scary for some children.

Attending the health assessment

- Take snacks and drinks – especially if it's an after school appointment.

- Take nappies and wipes, if needed.

- Take the child's favourite book or toy to pass the time.

After the health assessment

- Discuss the health plan with the doctor, so that you know what's expected from you.

- Check that the doctor has your address to send a copy of the health plan to you.

- Use the health plan that you have been sent as a "working document" that you can record updates on, so that you have all the information ready for the child's statutory LAC review.

Specialist health services for looked after children

Specialist health services for looked after children were first introduced in 2002, in response to a national Government initiative called *Quality Protects* (1999). This initiative was based on evidence that the health of children in the care system was not improving and children were leaving care with the same unmet health needs with which they entered.

The document *Promoting the Health of Looked After Children* was first published by the Department of Health in 2002 and was statutory for local authorities, but not for healthcare bodies. The recommendations became a statutory requirement for healthcare bodies in 2009, when the revised statutory guidance directed health providers to support local authorities in addressing health inequalities. The emphasis was now on the prevention of ill health and the improvement of health outcomes.

This statutory duty now placed on health services led to the introduction of specialist health teams for looked after children. These specialist teams consist of doctors and nurses with expertise and specialist knowledge and skills in looked after children's health and well-being.

Foster carers should work in partnership with their local specialist health teams to ensure that looked after children access and receive health services at the point of entry to care and throughout their time in care. Your social worker will be able to give you information and contact details should you require them for the child in your care.

3 Authority and consent

If a child is considered by health professionals to be competent to make their own decisions in relation to health treatments, they will be allowed to consent to them under the terms of "Gillick competence" (named after an associated legal case, *Gillick v West Norfolk* [1985]). The health professional will assess the child's capacity to understand the information they have been given using the "Gillick test" in order to make a decision about the treatment they are being offered. Children over 16 are assumed to be competent; however, a child over 16 with learning difficulties or impaired mental capacity may be assessed as not having "Gillick competence".

In the case of prescribing contraception to a girl under 16 without parental consent, a principle called "Fraser Guidelines" is applied by health professionals. These are the guidelines set out by Lord Fraser in his judgement of the above Gillick case in the House of Lords (1985).

Health professionals are trained to apply the principles of both Gillick competence and Fraser guidelines when working with children and young people, and will have regard for their ability to consent or to refuse consent.

> The NSPCC has a useful section on their website that provides easy-to-understand details about Gillick competence: https://learning.nspcc.org.uk/child-protection-system/gillick-competence-fraser-guidelines.

Delegated authority and consent

Consent is a fundamental requirement prior to any health intervention, be it a GP appointment, health assessment, routine outpatient appointment, or any medical or surgical intervention. In most instances, consent is implied when we attend at a planned appointment with a health professional; however, when we consider appointments that require an intervention or procedure, then consent has to be formally recorded following a discussion and explanation of the procedure and any risks. This is referred to as "informed consent".

In a situation where a child is under the age of 16 and consent is required for a health or medical intervention, it is the person holding parental responsibility for the child who gives this consent (unless the child is able to give their own consent, as in Gillick competence (see above)).

For many daily or routine activities and situations, foster carers will be required to exercise their responsibilities under "delegated authority". However, there may be occasions when, as a foster carer, you need to be aware of the differences between delegated authority and consent in relation to health and medical interventions, and also the law around parental responsibility.

Delegated authority and parental responsibility

Delegated authority and **parental responsibility** are two distinct things and are not interchangeable. Foster carers need to have a basic understanding of both in order to ensure that medical treatment for the child in their care is undertaken with consent, and that the person/s legally responsible for the child have given consent.

In simple terms, a woman who gives birth to a child is automatically given **parental responsibility**; this can only be removed in the case of adoption. A father has parental responsibility if:

- he was married to the mother at the time of the child's birth or married the mother subsequently;
- his name is on the birth certificate (applies to births registered after 1 December 2003);
- he has a parental responsibility agreement with the mother;
- by court order.

The child's parent with parental responsibility does not lose this when the child is looked after or voluntarily accommodated under section 20 of the Children Act 1989. A local authority has parental responsibility when a child is on a care order (interim or full) or when a child is on an emergency protection order.

The exception to obtaining consent prior to medical treatment is in the case of an emergency or life threatening situation. In such a case, health professionals will assess the need to act in such situations and can override the need for consent from those who have parental responsibility.

A foster carer never has parental responsibility; however, they may be able to act in certain situations on behalf of the person with parental responsibility – this is called **delegated authority**. The parameters of delegated authority are usually contained within the child's placement plan.

What is delegated authority in relation to health?

A social worker or person with parental responsibility can delegate authority to a foster carer, and this should be explicit in the permanence plan for the child. In principle, it means:

- having the authority to make day-to-day decisions depending on what has been delegated in the placement plan;
- identifying who has the authority to take particular decisions about the child; this should be recorded in the child's placement plan;
- the child's views should be taken into account in relation to delegated authority and consideration should be given as to whether a child is of an age and level of understanding to take some decisions themselves (Gillick competence).

In practice, delegated authority is individualised and will be defined in the placement plan for the child, a copy of which should be given to the foster carer. This may but not always include:

- visiting the dentist;
- visiting the optician;
- visiting the GP;
- any other health service provision, such as speech and language therapy, physiotherapy, dieticians, and sexual health services.

Immunisations are considered to be an invasive medical procedure requiring formal consent from the person/s with parental responsibility, or the child if Gillick competent.

Case example: gaining consent for a planned surgical procedure

Naseem is five years old, on a full care order, and has been living with his carers for two years. His class teacher at school has pointed out that she thinks there is a problem with Naseem's hearing, as he doesn't always respond when spoken to and can be distracted at times.

His foster carers have taken him to see the GP who, having examined Naseem, feels the likely cause is "glue ear", which is a build-up of fluid in the middle ear that can cause hearing problems. The GP has advised that the likely treatment will be grommets, which are tiny tubes that are inserted into the ear drums to treat the condition. This procedure will require a general anaesthetic.

The GP refers Naseem to an Ear, Nose and Throat (ENT) specialist at the local hospital.

The foster carers' role

- Ensure at every consultation at the child's GP that they are aware of the child's legal status and who holds parental responsibility.

- If the GP needs to refer a child to a specialist service for possible surgical intervention, make sure they have the correct contact details of the child's social worker, including their name, phone number, email and address.

- Inform the child's social worker immediately of the outcome of the consultation and the referral to a specialist.

- Once the appointment has been received, inform the child's social worker in order for the social worker to ensure that they can attend the appointment.

- Attend the appointment together with the child's social worker to discuss the procedure and to advise the specialist of who will consent for the child's surgery.

Different local authorities have different systems in place for signing consent for surgery; the child's social worker is responsible for identifying the appropriate social care professional with authority to sign the consent for surgery.

Foster carers do not have parental responsibility for children in their care and therefore cannot consent to surgical interventions. The parent/s or local authority holding parental responsibility will be required to sign consent for this.

Record keeping and confidentiality

The National Minimum Standards for fostering state that foster carers need to keep records that are clear, up to date, stored securely and that contribute to the understanding of the child or young person's life, including their health care needs.

- Information about children in foster care should always be kept confidential and only shared with those who have a legitimate and current need to know the information.

- Entries in records, decisions you or others have made about the child's care and reasons for these decisions need to be legible, clearly expressed and non-judgemental.

- It is important to distinguish clearly between fact, opinion and third party information.

- Every record you write should be signed and dated.

Information in relation to a child or young person's health and well-being (which includes any risk-taking behaviour) should be recorded clearly and in a way that will be helpful to the child when they access their files in the future. Children are actively encouraged to read their files, and it is therefore important that recordings use language that is professional and non-judgemental.

By using the statutory health plan as a "working document", carers can ensure that health needs and appointments or interventions are recorded in a timely manner, in order that any outstanding issues can be reviewed at the child's statutory LAC review (chaired by the IRO), and followed up by the health practitioner who completed the health assessment and plan. The child's social worker retains overall responsibility for monitoring the health plan.

Confidentiality has always been an issue that can cause great anxiety for children, young people and foster carers alike. It is essential that the boundaries of confidentiality are clearly understood by carers, children and young people. It is also important that children understand that confidentiality cannot be maintained in certain circumstances, for example, where there are safeguarding concerns. Carers should not make promises about this that cannot be kept.

The sharing of information is covered by legislation, principally the General Data Protection Regulation (GDPR) 2018 and the Data Protection Act 2018. The GDPR and Data Protection Act make reference to 'safeguarding of children and individuals at risk', which allows practitioners to share information without consent if necessary. Relevant personal information about the child or young person can be shared lawfully if it is to keep a child safe who is at risk from neglect, physical, emotional or sexual harm.

In terms of information sharing, it is important to remember that in the majority of serious case reviews (which are convened in the event of a child death as a result of abuse or neglect), a lack of information sharing is often cited as a contributory factor. Robust information sharing is the primary consideration in ensuring that the child or young person is safeguarded, and should be based on fact, not assumption, restricted to those who need to know, and recorded in writing. Information should be shared with consent wherever possible.

Remember that the GDPR and Data Protection Act are not a barrier to sharing information, but rather provide a framework to help organisations to share information appropriately.

Top tips

- Written information should be factual, timely and relevant.
- All records should be signed and dated.
- Errors should be crossed through with a single line and initialled and dated.
- Corrective fluid (such as Tippex) should not be used.
- Information, whether written or verbal, should be shared on a need-to-know basis only.

- Be aware of the environment – who is nearby who could potentially overhear information, e.g. it may not be advisable to talk about certain subjects in the school playground.

For further advice on information sharing, talk to your supervising social worker or visit your local Safeguarding Children's Partnership website.

4 Children's development at different ages

Health focus for children aged 0–5 years

Child development in the first five years is critical. Early childhood development covers aspects of, and the challenges of, feeding, sleeping, toileting, speech and language as well as common emotional and behavioural problems. 0–19 health practitioners (health visitors from a specialist public health service consisting of health professionals from different specialist practice areas) working in the community are ideally placed to work closely with families and children in order to identify any emerging problems and needs, and refer children to specialist services for additional support. The type of support offered may include referral to speech and language services, continence services (for toileting issues), play therapists, and sleep practitioners.

0–19 health practitioners are trained in recognising risk factors, concerns and signs of abuse. Their role includes contributing to multi-disciplinary meetings in relation to a child or family.

Key developmental milestones

Below are listed the key developmental milestones that a child is expected to reach during their first three years. These are some of the behaviours that health professionals will use to gauge a child's progress.

Newborn babies:

- Alertness and responsiveness – long periods of sleep interspersed with periods of wakefulness (fretfulness, crying and calmess).

- Posture and large movements – movements are mainly limited to arms and legs; newborn babies cannot support their own heads and therefore have "head lag".

- Primitive reflexes – the Moro reflex (babies' natural reaction to a loss of physical support), rooting and sucking, protective gag and cough, symmetrical palmar grasp[1] (all fade by six months, with the exception of the gag and cough reflex, which continues throughout life).

Aged 1 month:

- Emerging social smile (babies' intentional smile at a particular person).

- Baby fixes and follows a familiar face and maintains eye contact.

- Primitive reflexes are present.

Aged 3 months:

- Baby has head control when supported in a sitting position.

- Baby can visually follow a face or toy in a semi-circle.

- Baby looks at their own hands.

- Baby responds to cooing by the adult.

Aged 6 to 9 months:

- Baby is weight bearing when supported to stand.

- Baby rolls from front to back.

- Baby reaches out with one hand to grasp.

- Baby babbles, moving to tuneful babbling.

- Baby can search for a dropped toy within their visual field.

- Primitive reflexes have gone.

- Baby pulls to stand from sitting.

---

1   Symmetrical palmar grasp is a primitive reflex found in the first weeks of life, where an infant will automatically close both hands into a grasp position when the palm of the hand is stroked. This primitive reflex disappears at around the age of six–seven months when the infant learns to grasp, hold and release objects.

- Baby can use a pincer grip (index finger to thumb).
- Baby shows stranger wariness.
- Baby plays social games such as peek-a-boo.

Aged 12–15 months:

- Baby starts independent walking.
- Baby has mature finger grasp.
- Baby follows simple instructions like clapping.
- Baby can stack two cubes/play bricks.
- Baby's first words.
- Baby has functional use of toys.

Aged 18 months:

- Baby has emerging hand preference (left or right handedness).
- Baby has a range of single words.
- Baby follows simple directions, e.g. point to body parts.
- Baby has awareness of self-identity.
- Baby can imitate day-to-day activities at home.

Aged 2–2.5 years:

- Child runs safely, moving to jumping with two feet together.
- Child uses two-word combinations, progressing to using pronouns 'I' and 'you'.
- Child follows two-step instructions, and progressing to action words, e.g. jump.
- Child can do circular scribbling with a crayon, progressing to drawing a circle.
- Child mostly uses preferred hand (left or right handedness).
- Child turns pages of a book one at a time.

- Child throws and kicks a ball.

- Child provides verbal commentary during play.

    (Sheridan *et al*, 2014)

In accordance with the Healthy Child Programme (see below), the mandated reviews a child should receive include a new baby review, 6–8 week assessment, one year assessment, and 2–2.5 year review, which will refer to the above developmental milestones along with others.

Health focus for primary school aged children

By the time a child is ready to start primary school, between the ages of four and five years, they should be able to:

- Stand on one foot and hop.

- Hold a pencil in a tripod grasp.

- Draw a person with head, trunk, legs, arms and usually fingers.

- Relate recent experiences.

- Rote count to 20.

- Show sympathy for other children in distress.

- Recognise their own name in print.

- Skip and walk along a line.

- Copy shapes, and colour within outlines.

- Give their names and age.

- Engage in to-and-fro conversations.

- Has a friend.

    (Sheridan *et al*, 2014)

The National Childhood Measurement Programme (NCMP) was introduced in 2013 in response to growing concerns about the prevalence of childhood obesity in the UK. The programme involves weighing and measuring children in school reception year and Year 6. School entry screening is offered to all reception year pupils.

Foster carers are expected to respond positively to requests and invitations to discuss a looked after child's weight and growth management.

Health focus for secondary school aged young people

The health information covered for young people in this book relates to universal health interventions, such as immunisations, health promotion and health education. More specific health-related issues as a consequence of risk-taking behaviours such as smoking, drugs and alcohol are also discussed later on in this guide.

Healthy Child Programme

The Healthy Child Programme is a universal public health service to improve the health and well-being of all children through:

- health promotion;
- supporting parenting;
- health screening;
- immunisation programmes.

The programme is delivered by the health professionals working in the 0–19 years health service.

The overriding principle of the Healthy Child Programme is to reduce health inequalities and ensure that all children have equal access to universal health services that promote their health and development at key stages throughout their childhood.

The contribution of health visitor and school nursing services are key to the delivery of this programme. These services are based on four increasing levels of intervention:

- Community;

- Universal;

- Universal Plus (short-term additional help);

- Universal Partnership Plus (long-term multi-disciplinary support and safeguarding).

Initially, it is likely that a looked after child will be offered Universal Partnership Plus on entry to care as a result of their pre-care experiences, but this may vary depending on the locality. Once they are settled in care and have a robust care plan, these additional needs should resolve or be reduced to a level where the Universal Plus or Universal level of intervention will be thought more appropriate.

For looked after children, additional health screening is provided through the statutory health assessment process either by health visitors, school nurses or specialist looked after children's nurses.

As a foster carer, it is essential for you to ensure you know how to contact the 0–19 health service providers in your area. The specialist looked after children's health service can assist with this.

Health needs across all ages

Immunisations

Immunisations for children entering care are often incomplete, and as a foster carer you will be expected to be proactive in taking a child or young person for their immunisations. The immunisation schedule for children is constantly under review. For the current up-to-date schedule, visit www.nhs.uk or discuss this with your 0–19 health practitioner.

For looked after children, the signed consent for vaccinations should come from the person/s holding parental responsibility for the child. This may be a parent or a local authority representative. Whilst immunisations are part of the routine health surveillance programme, consent needs to be sought every time an immunisation opportunity arises. Some children will be fearful of immunisations, and involving them in discussions and decisions regarding their health and well-being in accordance with their age and understanding should be considered.

Bed wetting

Many children have issues with bed wetting (enuresis). Bed wetting is completely normal for children, and is often a phase they go through with little or no intervention needed from health professionals. However, for looked after children, due to their pre-care experiences, wetting the bed is more common and can be prolonged, requiring specialist enuresis interventions.

There are many causes associated with bed wetting. There may be a hereditary factor; children with parents who wet the bed as children are more likely to wet the bed themselves and may take more time to achieve permanent dryness.

For daytime wetting, consideration should be given as to whether the child has an underlying medical issue such as an overactive bladder or urinary tract infection, which in turn means more visits to the toilet in the day or wetting the bed. In the first instance, it will be important to rule out an underlying medical issue.

Once medical issues have been ruled out, simple measures can be taken to try to reduce and eventually resolve wetting.

Top tips

- Increase fluid intake by day. This improves the bladder capacity.

- DO NOT restrict fluids. Do not try to avoid bed wetting by stopping the child drinking. Children need to drink six–eight glasses of water a day to stay healthy.

- Positive praise. Always praise the child when they do manage to stay dry or remember to go to the toilet before they go to bed, for example.

- Avoid certain drinks, such as cola, fruit juice and caffeinated drinks, as these will stimulate the bladder.

If you think your fostered child's bed wetting is not improving or they are still wetting after the age of six, consult with your 0–19 health practitioner for advice and possibly a referral to a local enuresis clinic.

Constipation and soiling

Constipation is the most common bowel problem in children. It is not unusual for some children to hold a poo in and withhold going to the toilet for long periods. Looked after children may develop constipation as a result of poor diet and inadequate fluid intake, as well as emotional turmoil experienced prior to coming into care.

Constipation can be caused by withholding a poo; the poo gets bigger and harder and is therefore difficult and painful to pass.

If the child has previously passed a large, hard poo, this in turn may lead to the child holding on to a subsequent poo for as long as possible, to avoid pain; this then becomes a vicious circle that can be difficult to break.

A child with a sore bottom or an anal fissure (an anal tear probably caused by a previous large poo) may also avoid going for a poo because they fear it will be painful again, leading to the child holding on to the poo.

Sometimes constipation becomes so bad that it can cause faecal impaction, where a very big poo gets stuck in the rectum. Impaction can lead to soiling or overflow, which is when small bits of poo or runny poo can be seen in the child's pants. Overflow is often mistaken for diarrhoea. Other signs of impaction may be a loss of appetite, lack of energy, irritability, day or night time wetting, possible urinary tract infection, and a bloated tummy.

Soiling is sometimes referred to by health professionals as encopresis. The Children's Bowel and Bladder Charity (ERIC) states that the UK definition of encopresis is: 'The passage of a normal poo in an inappropriate place', for example, a child who chooses to do their poo in a place that is not the toilet, such as in their bedroom.

It is possible that constipation may contribute towards the child developing unusual poo habits.

Some children who have previously been toilet trained may go on to have issues of withholding poo, possibly due to a stressful experience, whereas others may have continuously soiled throughout their life.

Pooing and wetting issues are challenging, particularly for looked after children, as they may be tied into emotional and behavioural issues, and may take some time to resolve. Constipation and soiling may affect a looked after child's confidence and self-esteem, and may in some cases reduce their opportunities to enjoy social activities and treats like sleepovers or school trips; therefore these are issues that need to be resolved and will require sensitive handling and patience.

Top tips

- Drink plenty of water (fruit squash is OK too) – up to six–eight glasses a day.

- Eat five servings of different fruit and vegetables a day, as a minimum.

- Encourage the child to run around a lot; physical activity promotes digestion and increases metabolism, which aids bowel movement.

- For younger children, get the child into a routine where they sit on the toilet after every meal.

- Medication is sometimes required to make poo softer. If the child's GP prescribes medication for this, make sure it is taken by the child as prescribed.

- The health visitor/school nurse/specialist LAC nurse or child's GP are good sources of support.

For more information, visit ERIC – the children's bowel and bladder charity: www.eric.org.uk.

The CoramBAAF book, *Parenting a Child with Toileting Issues* (Fenton, 2019) has more useful information about this subject.

Speech, language and communication needs

At least 10 per cent of children have a speech and language need. Communication problems can impair the ability to interact, manage behaviour, learn and think. Common communication problems amongst looked after children include Autism Spectrum Disorder and Foetal Alcohol Spectrum Disorder.

Autism Spectrum Disorder

Children with Autism Spectrum Disorder (ASD) are often self-absorbed, and seem to exist in a private world where possibly they have limited ability to successfully communicate and interact with others. Children with ASD may have difficulty developing language skills and understanding of what others say to them. They may also have difficulty communicating non-verbally, such as through eye contact, and facial expressions.

Children with ASD may not have an ability to communicate or may have limited speaking skills, and this will depend on their intellectual and social development. Although some children may have rich vocabularies, many may have problems with the meaning and rhythm of words and sentences. Along with understanding body language and the meanings of different vocal tones, this may affect the ability of children with ASD to interact with others, especially people of their own age (National Institute on Deafness and other Communication Disorders, www.nidcd.nih.gov/health/autism-spectrum-disorder-communication-problems-children).

A number of charities provide advice and support on autism for parents and children, including the National Autistic Society – www.autism.org.uk.

The CoramBAAF book, *Parenting a Child with Autism Spectrum Disorder* (Carter, 2013) has useful information for parents and carers.

Foetal Alcohol Spectrum Disorder

Foetal Alcohol Spectrum Disorder (FASD) is the name given to encompass a variety of symptoms, factors or problems (which include Foetal Alcohol Syndrome (FAS)) that can potentially affect children if their mother consumed alcohol during the pregnancy. The World Health Organisation (WHO) suggests that approximately one in every 100 children worldwide is affected by FASD (Popova, 2017, pp. 313–388).

The signs of FASD can be physical and/or intellectual, and although alcohol can affect the development of all cells and organs, the brain is particularly vulnerable to the effects of alcohol exposure. As a result, these children and adults often experience difficulties in processing information. They may have difficulties with translating hearing into doing, thinking into saying, reading into speaking, or feeling into words (Adoption UK, 2018).

> A number of charities provide advice and support on FASD for parents and children, including the National Organisation for FASD – www.nofas-uk.org.
>
> The CoramBAAF books, *Parenting a Child Affected by Parental Substance Misuse* (Forrester, 2012), and *Dealing with Foetal Alcohol Spectrum Disorder* (Mather, 2018), have useful information for parents and carers.

The effect of communication needs on children

In areas of high social deprivation, around 50 per cent of children have been found to start school with limited language, and those with severe behavioural issues have been found to have communication needs. Research has shown that looked after children have higher than average levels of speech, language and communication needs (Law *et al*, 2011). Those young people with a speech, language and communication need gain half as many GCSEs as their peers.

In addition, 60–90 per cent of young people who are involved with the youth justice services have been found to have a speech, language and communication need (Bryan, 2004).

Communication difficulties could present as difficulties with vocabulary and word finding, sequencing of sentences, lack of emotional literacy, and problems with social communication. All of this leads to stress and frustration for the child, problems with misunderstanding "jokes", difficulties in negotiating, difficulties maintaining friendships, and difficulties in finding and securing employment.

When working with or caring for children and young people with speech, language and communication needs, Cook (2017) suggests some strategies that you can try:

- Frequently checking their understanding of what you have said, by asking them to explain it in their own words.

- Using short and simple language when asking questions, incorporating a real-life example where possible.

- Being direct with questions and avoiding using idioms where possible, e.g. 'I'm over the moon'.

- Consider using visual aids to explain potentially confusing concepts.

If you are concerned about a child's speech and language development, contact the child's GP, 0–19 health practitioner or a member of the specialist looked after children's health team.

> For more information about children's communication development, visit: https://ican.org.uk

Sleep

Sleep for babies, children and teenagers is fundamental to healthy child development, and something that can be taken for granted as being natural and mostly uneventful, especially once a baby starts to sleep through at night; and yet from our experience it is perhaps one of the most commonly identified problems found at initial and review health assessments of looked after children.

'When a child is having sleep issues it can impact on all areas of their development, including their emotional, physical and mental health', according to the Children's Sleep Charity (www.thechildrenssleepcharity.org.uk).

Children who come into care have often experienced irregular sleep patterns and poor sleep habits as a result of their pre-care experiences. These experiences include anxiety and depession in parents, stressful home environments, poor bedtime routines, diets that contain high levels of "E" numbers/sugar and caffeine, and foods that hinder sleep, as well as high levels of anxiety in the child.

The impact of poor sleep on a child's development is significant and can lead to children exhibiting challenging behaviours both in and out of school, as well as higher than normal levels of poor concentration, irritability and an inability to process information. This in turn will have a detrimental effect on academic achievement and an impact on their emotional health and well-being.

Children's sleep problems can also impact on other members of the fostering household, who may themselves experience higher levels of fatigue throughout the day and an inability to concentrate in the work environment, due to their sleep having been disturbed by the child.

Children may experience sleep problems secondary to other factors, such as contact with birth family members, substance and alcohol misuse, missing from home episodes and the use of social media and mobile phones around bedtime. Some of these behaviours are considered to be risk-taking behaviours and can lead to young people making negative lifestyle choices.

For all these reasons, it is very important to understand and promote sleep for children and young people in foster care.

Sleep problems can be divided into two types: settling and waking. These problems can be caused by a variety of factors, and it follows that a variety of strategies and treatments are required to resolve or reduce symptoms of sleep disturbances.

It is important to note that if you suspect your foster child is unwell, you should delay starting any strategies or routines until they are well again. It should also be noted that children with disabilities and complex emotional needs may not respond to the following suggested routines, and it would be advisable to seek help and support from a more specialist sleep practitioner to address sleep problems.

If a child in foster care continues to struggle with sleep, after they have had time to settle into the placement, you could consider making small changes in two areas: firstly, what a child eats and drinks around bedtime; and secondly, the bedtime routine itself.

Food and drink to aid sleep

It is know that tryptophan, an essential amino acid, aids sleep, along with melatonin, a natural hormone, which is produced by the body after nightfall.

Dairy products and oats contain tryptophan, so a bedtime snack such as warm milk or even a small portion of porridge (minus sugar) would be a good choice. "Alternative" milk such as oat, soya or almond milk can be substituted for children who do not have dairy for cultural or allergy reasons.

Bananas are a good source of melatonin and also contain magnesium, which aids muscle relaxation. An option to promote sleep would be, dependent on the child's age, mashed bananas and warm milk at supper time.

Often, parents and carers will give children cereals as a supper time food. However, when you consider that cereals are typically a breakfast time food, intended to provide energy at the start of the day (due in part to their often containing high levels of sugar), it becomes obvious as to why they then can adversely affect sleep. Eating cereal at bedtime will cause a spike in energy too close to bedtime and may therefore have a counter effect on relaxation and sleep.

Caffeine, which is found in hot chocolate and fizzy drinks as well as tea and coffee, is a stimulant, and therefore wherever possible should be avoided at bedtime, along with fruit and fruit juices. The latter contain fructose, which is again a source of sugar that can give a rush of energy.

Supper time snacks should be eaten in small quantities, as eating a large portion of food before bedtime can make it difficult to sleep. As most children go to bed earlier than adults, the last meal of the day should not be a heavy meal.

Remember the saying: "Breakfast like a king, lunch like a prince and dine like a pauper": this is actually sound advice when you consider the length of time it takes the gut to digest food.

Bedtime routines

A bedtime routine for children is absolutely essential and should be as consistent as possible to ensure stability is in place. The bedtime routine should be followed by everyone involved in the care of the child. Ideally, to establish the routine, which may take up to a fortnight, one carer should take the lead to implement the routine to ensure consistency until it is established and improvement in sleep patterns is seen.

- Bath time should be approximately 30 minutes before bedtime. It should be a soothing and relaxing experience, not over-exciting or stimulating: remember, the purpose is to help the child to relax.

- After the bath, avoid taking the child back into the living room where a TV may be on or other members of the family may be. This ensures that the relaxed child is not exposed to further stimulation.

- The child's bedroom should be comfortably warm and dark; you may want to consider using a soothing night light. Ensure that there are no TVs or other screens, e.g. tablets, left on. If you have a mobile phone, turn it to silent and put it away or face down to avoid the screen lighting up.

- If the child is given a bedtime drink of milk, it should be ready to be given in the child's bedroom.

- A bedtime story is a great way to end the day, but choose a book that is not too long, that is calming and that does not require any interaction from the child.

- Once you have given supper and read the child their story, put them to bed, but do not stay longer than necessary. This is the time at which the child needs to learn to fall asleep by themselves, so that if they do wake in the night, they can fall back to sleep by themselves.

- Leave the bedroom, reassuring the child that you will see them in the morning.

This routine can of course be individualised in relation to the child's age and level of understanding. Actual bed times should be adjusted to reflect the child's age.

Carers need to have faith in themselves and the changes they are making in order to change a child's sleep pattern. This is a process, and like many other processes it will take time to establish.

Because we know that this process can be frustrating and disheartening to begin with, it is a good idea to make a note of how many times in an evening you have had to go back into the child's bedroom to put them back to bed or reassure them that you are still there. This will enable you to see the progress you are making from one night to the next. You may find that at the start of implementing the routine, you had to go into the room 20 times to resettle the child, but by night four, for example, this reduced to 12 times, which will help you to see the progress you have made and to stick with the routine.

For preschool children, health visitors are a great resource when it comes to promoting bedtime routines and sleep management. Do seek advice from them if needed. For school aged children, the school nurse or specialist looked after children's nurses are there to help and support.

Adolescents and sleep

It is important to understand that during puberty, changes occur in the way the brain regulates the timing of sleep, which manifests itself in a later bedtime and tiredness throughout the day for many young people. This is because adolescents need as much sleep as they did in middle childhood, which is approximately nine hours a night. This change in sleep pattern is often referred to as a "phase delay" (Berk, 2010) and actually strengthens throughout puberty; it is compounded by the use of social media and mobile phone usage late into the night. Limiting internet access by, for instance, switching off wi-fi and establishing ground rules about handing in mobile phones at bedtime can help reduce the symptoms of "phase delay".

If, as a fostering household, you have these ground rules in place for everyone when a young person is first introduced, they may be more accepting of the idea, and see it as part of the "norm" for the household. Most children and young people want to fit in and feel included in the family routines. However, for some young people, handing in their mobile phones can feel like a punishment, so be prepared for some resistance and negotiation. Your supervising social worker and the young person's social worker are good allies to have when addressing limiting access to mobile phones and social media at bedtime, so don't be afraid to ask for their support and guidance.

Top tips

- Establish what type of sleep problem the child has, i.e. settling or waking.

- Keep a sleep diary to help you see patterns and factors that affect sleep as well as to record progress.

- Preparation is the key to success: make changes to diet, drinks and bedtime routines and stick with them.

- Get the whole family on board with the changes you want to make and agree on who will be the main carer for this.

- Talk it through with other professionals and get your support in place – this isn't going to be easy!

- Set ground rules for the household around wi-fi access and mobile phone curfews.

- Seek specialist support for more entrenched and complex sleep problems.

For more information and advice on sleep, visit: www.thechildrenssleepcharity.org.uk.

The CoramBAAF book, *Parenting a Child Affected by Sleep Issues* (Vaughan and Burnell, 2020 (forthcoming) has useful information for parents and carers.

Food and activity

Learning about healthy eating should take place from an early age in order to equip young people and adults with the skills and knowledge they need to ensure they can make positive choices in relation to their diet.

The nutritional needs for children in foster care are the same as for those not in the care system, but the pre-care experiences these children could have encountered may mean that there are additional requirements that need to be considered. It may be that food has been used for comfort by the child in the past, or that there has been no food available and children have been or are malnourished. Further to this, children's past experiences of meal times, if they existed in their birth families, may reflect the chaos of pre-care family life. The lack of a healthy diet in the past may have impacted on the child's education, concentration and attendance at school.

Your role as a foster carer is to help children and young people view food and eating as a positive experience, and encourage habits and attitudes that will support these young people on leaving care.

The National Minimum Standards for Fostering (2011) state that foster carers should understand the child's health needs and how to maintain a healthy lifestyle. Children should be encouraged to participate in a range of activities that contribute to improving their physical and mental health, and should be helped to lead healthy lifestyles. The Standards recognise that children entering care may also have significant issues around food and eating due to their pre-care experiences.

Children from different cultural backgrounds should be offered foods according to their cultural needs. It is important to have food available that is familiar to them, as well as ensuring that, as a foster carer, you are able and willing to provide a diet that is consistent with the health needs of the children and young people in your care. As a newly approved foster carer, you are not expected to have the knowledge to provide food choices that are not consistent with your family's diet, but to be able to seek advice and support from the relevant professionals, such as your supervising social worker and health care professionals.

Childhood obesity

Childhood obesity is significant to the health of children and has serious implications for both their mental and physical health (Public Health England, 2018).

It is recognised that obesity in children contributes to:

- emotional and behavioural needs;
- bullying;
- low self-esteem;
- school absence;
- high cholesterol;
- high blood pressure;
- pre diabetes;
- bone and joint problems;
- breathing difficulties;
- obesity in adulthood;
- premature death.

Very few children become overweight because of an underlying medical condition. Type 2 diabetes (for which being overweight and inactive can be contributing factors) is being seen more and more in children and young people and has lifetime implications.

The Eat Well Guide (renamed from the Eat Well Plate) is a handy tool to ensure the right balance of nutrients for children. For more information, visit: www.nhs.uk/the-eatwell-guide.

Top tips

- Encourage children and young people to eat a wide variety of foods without adding salt, sugar or honey.

- Eat together as a family and set a good example with the food choices you make.

- Keep a well-stocked fruit bowl and have a ready supply of prepared vegetables, such as carrot sticks and peppers, for healthy snacks.

- For the picky eater, disguise finely chopped vegetables in foods such as soups or sauces.

- Encourage active play.

It is important to note that overweight children do not need to do more exercise than children of a healthy weight. Their extra body weight means that they will naturally burn more calories for the same activity.

NHS Choices recommends that physical activity needs to include both aerobic activity and exercise to strengthen muscles and bones.

For children and young people aged 5–18:

- Aim for an average of at least 60 minutes a day of varied types of moderate intensity physical activity.

- Several short 10-minute, or even five-minute, bursts of activity throughout the day can be just as good as an hour-long stretch.

- Aim to spread activity throughout the day. All activities should make you breathe faster and feel warmer.

- Reduce sedentary behaviour and screen time.

Body image and healthy eating issues

The term "eating disorder" refers to a range of eating-related problems such as anorexia nervosa, bulimia nervosa, selective eating, and overeating. These behaviours can be a young person's way of expressing distress, and are linked to negative beliefs about themselves and their world. Many looked after children are likely to have had negative pre-care experiences that affect their self-esteem, confidence and how they believe others see them. Eating disorders can be a very distressing experience for a young person, and they may feel that they cannot share their concerns and feelings with anyone.

Both anorexia nervosa and bulimia nervosa are characterised by dissatisfaction with a person's body and size, which can possibly lead to a desire to achieve an unattainable level of thinness, and a dread of fatness. It has been suggested that dieting amongst teenagers, even at a moderate level, is the most important predictor of new eating disorders occurring among adolescents (Patten *et al*, 1999).

Encouraging exercise rather than dieting as a means of weight control is therefore particularly important among children and young people.

The Caroline Walker Trust (which is dedicated to the improvement of public health through good food) recommends the following:

- Concerns about eating disorders in young people should be taken seriously and medical help and advice sought.

- Anorexia nervosa and bulimia nervosa both require specialist help. The first point of contact is the young person's GP, who can refer them on to a specialist service.

What carers can do

- Encourage physical activity rather than dieting among young people who are concerned about their body shape.

- Children and young people with eating disorders may find it difficult to communicate with those around them and may find an independent helpline useful, such as www.youngminds.org.uk.

- Always consult with a health professional should you be concerned about a young person.

Ask for further advice from the specialist looked after children's team or 0–19 health practitioner for consideration of a referral to healthy lifestyle resources or local activities and services.

> For more information on healthy eating for children and adults, visit: www.nhs.uk/change4life/.

Oral health

Oral health is important for all children to enable them to feel physically, mentally and socially engaged.

Looked after children have significantly higher levels of tooth decay than their peers, and this is an important health inequality to address. For many looked after children, attention to oral health and dental care will have been lacking in their early lives. There continue to be barriers to achieving good oral health for children in the care system, such as frequency of placement changes, leading to delay in dental referrals for specialist dental care, and inequalities in commissioning and funding NHS dental services in different locality areas.

For the child, the barriers could be inconsistency of dental hygiene routines, never having been properly taught how to brush their teeth, strong taste of toothpaste which deters the child from brushing, or anxieties about visiting the dentist and what that might entail, to name but a few.

Basic steps to maintaining good oral health

- Listen and talk to the child about their anxieties around oral health.

- Support the child to brush their teeth twice daily with fluoride toothpaste as soon as teeth come through. Carers should continue active involvement in tooth brushing until the child is seven years of age (or older, depending on the child's level of comprehension).

- If the child does not like the mint taste of traditional toothpaste, you could see if they prefer a fruity flavoured children's toothpaste, or one of the neutral flavoured ones that are now available.

- After brushing, spit but do not rinse the mouth (to retain the benefit of the toothpaste for longer).

- Take the child to the dentist before they are one year old, or when the first tooth erupts, and then regularly for check-ups and possibly fluoride varnish application.

- Older children may require a couple of introductory visits to the dental practice before they have a check up, to reassure them and to answer any questions they may have.

- Reduce sugar consumption in food and drinks; this includes when weaning babies.

- Do not give sugary drinks through teated bottles or feeder cups as this is likely to promote tooth decay.

- Water is the best drink for oral health.

For more information about oral health, visit: www.nhs.uk.

Emotional health and well-being

Studies have consistently established that more than half of children in care, regardless of where they reside in the Western World, have mental health problems of sufficient scale and severity to warrant the provision of mental health services.

(Tarren-Sweeney, 2011)

For a number of reasons, the emotional and mental health of children in the care system is a cause for concern. Statistically, looked after children and care leavers are significantly more likely than their peers to experience mental health problems. For the majority of these children, their pre-care experiences will have triggered emotional turmoil which, if left unchecked, may go on to manifest itself as mental illness.

A recent development in professional thinking and understanding of how the mental health of children is affected by their experience has resulted in the introduction of the term "Adverse Childhood Experiences" (ACEs). In the simplest of terms, ACEs can be categorised as exposure to:

- domestic abuse;
- drug and/or alcohol abuse;
- familial mental health issues;
- physical, emotional and/or sexual abuse;
- neglect;
- loss due to separation or divorce of parents;
- loss due to bereavement;
- incarceration of a family member.

Added to this list is entering the care system.

It is widely thought that, in all likelihood, a child who experiences one ACE will experience other ACEs, as many of the circumstances listed above do not exist in isolation. The outcomes for children affected by ACEs can be devastating, affecting their long-term potential and outcomes.

It therefore follows that the likelihood of a child coming into your care with one or more ACEs is very high, and consideration needs to be given to how we recognise the signs of children being adversely affected by ACEs, and how we respond as a team around the child.

Children who have experienced four or more ACEs have a substantially higher possibility of engaging in risk-taking behaviours, such as illicit drug use, alcohol addiction and attempted suicide, and this risk further increases for children who have experienced six or more ACEs.

Even with experiencing fewer than four ACEs, there is an increased risk of children engaging in behaviours that harm health, which may include binge drinking, poor diet, smoking, unplanned teenage pregnancy, violence, intravenous drug use, and entering the criminal justice system.

While this is a bleak prognosis, the impact of ACEs on children can be minimised with the right support in place. As a foster carer, you are uniquely placed as a member of the team around the child to build a child's resilience to trauma, which will in the long term help them to go on to experience a happier, healthier and more fulfilled life.

Assessing a child's emotional health

One way of assessing emotional health is by using Goodman's Strengths and Difficulties Questionnaire (SDQ) (1997) as a screening tool. This tool should be used by the organisations concerned in the assessment of emotional health in looked after children; in some areas, it is used at the initial health assessment as a baseline measure and then repeated at intervals that should fall in line with the child's statutory health assessments.

Whatever the interval between screenings, as a foster carer, you will be asked to complete the screening tool provided by your fostering service, giving a balanced response to the questions, based on your experience of caring for the child. The questionnaire is simple, does not require any training, and should take only five to ten minutes to complete. You will be supported by the child's social worker or your supervising social worker to complete this. It is good practice to have other professionals, such as social workers and teachers who are involved with the child, complete an SDQ at the same time, in order to gain a holistic understanding of the child's emotional status.

When a child presents with more complex and challenging behaviours, a referral to a specialist Child and Adolescent Mental Health Service (CAMHS) might be an appropriate response. Unfortunately, due to high demand for CAMHS, there is often a lengthy waiting list, and many carers and professionals are looking to identify alternative therapies, strategies and interventions to support children whilst they are waiting for CAMHS interventions.

There will be occasions when CAMHS will decide that it is not appropriate to work directly with a child, and it may be that an indirect therapeutic approach is more appropriate. You, as the child's foster carer, may be identified as the best person to undertake this approach. In such cases, you will be supported to use interventions that support a therapeutic parenting style.

In some areas, resourcing has been provided to commission specialist looked after children CAMHS, which are multi-disciplinary teams of professionals. These teams take an individual or tiered approach to offering services, depending on a child's need. These approaches can range between "Brief intervention" to "Multi-systemic intervention".

It is important that, as a foster carer, you develop your understanding of emotional and mental health issues for children in your care. Wider reading and training opportunities, such as the training your fostering service offers, are invaluable in developing your knowledge and skills in this area.

For more information, visit: www.youngminds.org.uk.

The CoramBAAF book, *The Foster Carer's Guide to Parenting Teenagers* (Bond, 2019), has more information on therapeutic interventions used with young people.

The CoramBAAF book, *Parenting a Child with Emotional and Behavioural Difficulties* (Hughes, 2012), has more information on this subject.

Sexual health and relationships

The thought of discussing sexual health and relationships with our own children can be quite daunting, with a possible level of awkwardness and embarrassment on both sides. As a foster carer, there is an expectation that you will be directly involved in discussions around sexual health and relationships with a variety of children who have potentially been involved in or witnessed negative and abusive behaviours at one end of the scale, to those who have no level of understanding of sex or relationships at the other. In addition, we all have our own beliefs and attitudes around this subject, and those beliefs and attitudes will influence how we respond to certain situations.

A large percentage of children in care will have experienced domestic abuse within the home. For many, this abuse will have become "normalised" and they will struggle to recognise the negative impact this has had or will have on their own relationships. It is very important that from the outset, positive role modelling and respectful relationships are promoted in your home.

What we do know through evidence gathered over many years is that looked after children are over-represented when it comes to teenage pregnancy, sexual exploitation and also in relation to domestic abuse situations. It is therefore essential that foster carers equip themselves with knowledge, training and skills to embark upon this necessary area of support in fostering.

Of course, getting the conversation started can be a stumbling block, as often children need stability and security in placements before they will feel comfortable in speaking openly and asking for help. Do not let this put you off – there will be "natural" opportunities to get the conversation started, for example, whilst watching age-appropriate TV programmes, where these issues are played out on screen. Use this as an opportunity to ask the child in your care what their thoughts are on the situation being dramatised, possible outcomes, possible barriers, or support that is available.

Wherever possible, keep this conversational, and give positive feedback about the child's thought processes or understanding of the issues. This dialogue will then become natural between you and your foster child and will help to open up other avenues of conversation.

If you are struggling to open up conversations with your child, try some of the online resources that cover a range of topics. A really good and accessible YouTube video that covers the sensitive issue of consent and sex for young people can be found by searching online for "YouTube tea and consent (Thames Valley Police)".

There are many other topics online and websites that will help with these conversations. For instance, a range of resources can be found at: www.fpa.org.uk/relationships-and-sex-education.

The range of issues around sexual health and relationships affecting children in today's society are complex, with an increased awareness of gender, sexuality, coercive controlling behaviours, sexual exploitation, grooming, and online abuse, including indecent images. At times, it can feel overwhelming for foster carers and professionals alike. Therefore, accessing Sexual Health and

Relationship (SHR) training is very important for everyone working with and supporting looked after children.

A recent research study (Nixon *et al*, 2019) highlighted the importance of SHR training and policies to avoid role ambiguity, particularly when there is a lack of clarity about what is expected of carers. In particular, this relates to the use of SHR policies that support carer discussions, and allow carers to fulfil their "corporate parenting" responsibilities.

Bond (2019) states:

> *Your task is to support them [children and young people] to feel comfortable and accepting of their own sexuality and to grow up aware of their rights to enjoy their bodies. Whilst keeping themselves safe...*

Another important finding of the Nixon study mentioned above was that foster carers and social care practitioners identified three areas that caused increased anxieties around conflicts within their role which could potentially be barriers to SHR discussions:

- balancing child protection concerns with undertaking preventative SHR discussions;
- potential for allegations to be made against carers and practitioners;
- carers reconciling their personal beliefs, such as religious and moral beliefs, against their responsibility to discuss SHR.

Child sexual exploitation (CSE) hit the headlines in 2012 with the media coverage of an investigation into and subsequent prosecution of 19 men on charges of CSE in Rochdale. This case was a watershed for investigations and prosecutions across the UK and has been followed by several others. Perhaps the most distressing case was that occuring in Rotherham in 2014, which involved CSE in the area between 1997 and 2013, shocking the public by the sheer scale of the investigation, which involved 1,400 children.

As a result of these and worryingly many other recent CSE cases, indicators and signs of CSE have been identified by the organisations concerned. Here are just a few that should be considered when caring for looked after children, who are at increased risk of being exploited. It should be noted that both boys and girls can be victims of CSE:

- frequently going missing from home or school;

- going out late at night and not returning until morning;

- being picked up in cars by unknown males;

- a significantly older boyfriend, girlfriend or friend;

- unexplained money, possessions, mobile phone credit or a new or second mobile phone;

- increased use of mobile phone and/or increased internet activity;

- regularly going out and drinking alcohol and/or taking drugs.

> For further information on CSE and the signs to look out for, visit: www.nspcc.org.uk/what-is-child-abuse/types-of-abuse/child-sexual-exploitation.
>
> The CoramBAAF books *Caring for a Child who has been Sexually Exploited* (Fursland, 2017), and *The Foster Carer's Handbook on Parenting Teenagers* (Bond, 2019), have useful information for parents and carers on, respectively, CSE and sex and relationships.

It is no wonder that foster carers can feel overwhelmed and at times anxious about their role, but help is at hand, and the team around the child is a good place to start when caring for looked after children whom you fear may be showing signs of CSE or of being "groomed" for CSE.

In addition, there are some fundamental principles that underpin practice for foster carers that will support you in your role as an educator and trusted adult in order to protect children in your care.

- Access training: this is essential for all carers and should not be limited to mandatory training modules provided by your fostering service. Training can be classroom-based, or through e-learning opportunities, which may be more convenient for foster carers.

- Engage in supervision with your supervising social worker: this is a learning opportunity and will develop your professional practice as well as your confidence.

● Record all details about the child in a timely manner, in accordance with record-keeping practice. This will be useful to discuss at supervision and also, if appropriate, at the child's looked after (LAC) review.

● Share information with professionals around the child: communication is key to safer outcomes for children, particularly in relation to sexual health and relationships.

In the previous chapter, Gillick competence and Fraser guidelines were explained; these principles underpin practice around consent in relation to sexual health and relationships. There are a couple of situations where the rule of law overrides these principles, and foster carers need to be absolutely clear about their role and responsibilities.

● The act of any child under the age of 13 years involved in sexual activity is classed as statutory rape, as defined by the Sexual Offences Act 2003. As a foster carer, you have a duty to inform children's services and the police of any concerns that a child in your care is sexually active if they are under 13 years of age.

● "Sexting" is the sending of a sexual photo to someone else via email, online messaging or text, usually by mobile phone. If any person, irrespective of their age, has a sexual photo of another person under the age of 18 years on their phone, they are classed as being in possession of an indecent image of a child, as defined by the Sexual Offences Act 2003. This applies whether or not the image is of a boyfriend or girlfriend. The sending of an image (sexual photo) of a child is classed as distribution, irrespective of the circumstances in which the image was sent, e.g. if, as a foster carer, you become aware of an image on a child's phone and send it to the social worker or the police as evidence, you are technically classed as distributing an indecent image of a child and could face prosecution.

Always speak to a social worker in the first instance before acting. Guidance will be given to ensure the child's and your safety in these situations.

> The Think U Know website is an excellent resource on this subject for carers, children and young people – visit: thinkuknow.co.uk.
>
> The CoramBAAF book, *The Foster Carer's Handbook on Parenting Teenagers* (Bond, 2019), has useful information on this subject for parents and carers.

Substance misuse

The term substance misuse refers to taking substances that may harm health or reduce a person's ability to function in society. Most teenagers will experiment with substances, e.g. drugs and/or alcohol, at some point.

Substance misuse amongst young people in care is a real concern for all professionals. As a foster carer, you may well be the first to recognise that there is a problem. Factors that will influence and increase the risk of substance misuse are complex and can be deep-rooted. For example, the child in your care may have come from a home where drug or alcohol misuse was prevalent. They may see it as the "norm", and therefore they are more likely to be involved in substance misuse than their peers.

Nationally, there has been an increase in the age of children entering care in recent years: 39 per cent of children in care in England in 2018 were aged 10–15 years, and 24 per cent were aged 16 years and over (Department for Education, 2019b, 2019c). It is therefore worth considering that there may be an increased number of children and young people who are already misusing substances such as drugs, alcohol or tobacco when they first enter care.

Looked after children may have had pre-care experiences that have been associated with substance misuse, and this may have been one of the reasons for a child entering care. Additional factors that will exacerbate substance misuse issues include frequent placement moves, being away from family and friends, not accessing education, and feeling that they have no one to turn to for support.

The impact of peer pressure in this area should never be underestimated, particularly for children and young people who are seeking an identity within society. This is a significant factor for looked after children, who often struggle with their self-identity and fitting in with their peers, and who are therefore more susceptible to peer pressure.

Adolescence can be a difficult time for any young person as they navigate their way to adulthood. This is compounded further for young people in the care system, who may not have had the benefit of positive role models to develop their self-esteem and emotional resilience.

For some young people, drugs are used as a way of relieving stress or masking distressing thoughts and feelings that they may be experiencing. It can therefore be difficult to influence a change in behaviours around substance misuse, as a young person may use this as a coping mechanism. It is also known that teenagers experience a higher level of impulsivity and limitations in consequential thinking, linked to the ongoing development of the adolescent brain.

Young people who use substances to a lesser degree for recreational purposes may come to no harm in relation to long-term health outcomes. However, they will still require support, education and interventions from professionals, especially foster carers, who are well placed to do this.

Drugs and the law

The Misuse of Drugs Act 1971 classifies drugs into three categories – A, B and C. Drugs can be moved up or down the classification range; an example of this was in 2004 when cannabis was downgraded from class B to class C, but subsequently in 2009 was reclassified as a class B drug. But this does not mean young people cannot still be charged with a criminal offence if found in possession of cannabis. The classification of drugs is used as an aid to sentencing around offences of possession and supply.

Whilst the classification of a drug may change, the law does not, and irrespective of classification, the use of non-prescribed drugs remains illegal. Young people in your care may have quite a lot of knowledge of drugs from their peers, or from their pre-care experiences, and are unlikely to listen to you if you aren't up to date in your knowledge.

For more information on this subject, along with advice and guidance, visit: www.talktofrank.com.

The CoramBAAF book, *The Foster Carer's Handbook on Parenting Teenagers* (Bond, 2019) has useful information on this subject for parents and carers.

Alcohol

Substance misuse among young people in the UK has been broadly in decline since 2001 (Aynsley *et al,* undated); however, alcohol and cannabis remain the most commonly used substances amongst adolescents.

Alcohol use is higher in looked after children than in their peers who are not in care, and looked after children aged 11–19 years who have been in care have a fourfold increased risk of drug and alcohol use compared to children not in care. This rather worrying finding is evidenced by NICE guidance produced in 2014. The guidance resulted from a study of approximately 21,000 young people accessing specialist drug and alcohol services, which identified looked after children as counting for seven per cent of the total of the group.

Risk factors that influenced substance and alcohol misuse for the group as a whole (both looked after and non-looked after children) were:

- poor mental health;
- school failure and early parenthood;
- parental poverty;
- absence of support networks;
- parental substance use;
- poor maternal mental health;
- early family disruption; and
- in the majority of cases, abuse and/or neglect for looked after young people.

It is known that alcohol reduces inhibitions and affects cognitive thinking; this in turn increases the risk of engagement in risk-taking behaviours, as well as increasing vulnerabilities in young people whilst under the influence of alcohol. This includes behaviours such as drink driving, or getting into cars driven by young people who have been drinking, as well as increasing the risk of having unprotected sex. Whilst these are impulsive actions taken whilst under the influence of drink, the long-term repercussions can be life changing and, in worst case scenarios, fatal.

Because brain development continues into the mid-twenties, early introduction to alcohol can greatly increase the risk of damaging the developing brain as well as increasing addictive tendencies. Young people under 15 years of age are particularly at risk, because during this period the developing brain undergoes the most change in the frontal lobe and hippocampus, which are associated with motivation, impulse control and addiction (Better Health Channel, 2015).

There are strategies that foster carers can implement that will support and have a positive and protective impact on young people engaging in alcohol misuse or any other risk-taking behaviours. These include:

- providing a positive and supportive family environment;
- developing a social support system for the young person;
- encouraging positive relationships with friends;
- ensuring that there is at least one adult whom the young person can go to for support;
- supporting a young person to remain in education, employment or training.

As a foster carer, you should discuss with your social worker how to support a young person if you have concerns about alcohol misuse.

It is also worth noting that, as a foster carer, you need to consider your position as a role model to young people in your care. Think about your own behaviours around alcohol and drinking in front of children and young people. Consideration should also be given to your ability to drive a car in the event of an emergency, if you have consumed alcohol.

For more information about alcohol and how this can affect young people, along with advice and guidance, visit: www.youngminds.org.uk.

Smoking

Over the last two decades, the number of young people smoking has fallen. In 2018, 16 per cent of 11–15-year-olds smoked, as compared to 23 per cent in 2012 (Action on Smoking and Health (ASH), 2019).

There are a number of factors that influence children and young people to start smoking. Young people who truant or who are excluded from school are twice as likely to smoke as their peers who are in school. Young people who use illegal substances are again more likely to smoke, and there is a question about whether smoking cigarettes can be a first step toward smoking cannabis.

Young people's attitudes to smoking have changed over time, with many feeling that smoking is affected by peer pressure, or a way to look cool in front of friends. What is perhaps more worrying is that, in a survey undertaken in 2018 by ASH (Action on Smoking and Health) (2019), 95 per cent of young people who smoked cigarettes reported that they did so because it helped them with stress and helped them to relax, and 80 per cent smoked because they felt that they were addicted. These findings strongly indicate that many young people are smoking as a coping mechanism and that the addictive tendencies are beginning to surface at this early age.

The younger a person is when they start to smoke, the greater the long-term health risks of lung cancer and heart disease.

In addition to the risks of young people smoking is the associated harm from passive smoking. There is a robust evidence base that children living in the poorest households (where there is a higher level of smoking) have the highest levels of exposure to second-hand smoke. This, in turn, increases the incidence of bronchitis, pneumonia, asthma, glue ear, and sudden infant death (SID) in infants and children.

These findings support the CoramBAAF recommendations (2018) that most fostering services apply when approving new foster carers, that children under five years of age (who spend more time at home than school aged children, and who are most susceptible to the adverse health effects of passive smoking) should effectively not be placed with carers who smoke or who have a member of the fostering household who smokes.

Foster carers are in a key position to support young people who smoke and be positive role models for the young people in their care. It is important to treat smoking as seriously as you would the use of other substances.

As part of the annual health assessment process for the child, there should be an assessment of potential exposure to substance misuse, including smoking, using a recommended screening tool. This will provide an opportunity to give early targeted support to the child, which can reduce the likelihood of future drug misuse. The child's health plan should set out any actions or referrals to specialist services, and you should ensure that you have a copy so that you are aware of any responsibilities you have in relation to this.

For more information about smoking, visit: www.ash.org.

Unaccompanied asylum-seeking children

Over the last decade, there has been an increase in the number of children and young people entering the care system under the definition of being an unaccompanied asylum-seeking child. An unaccompanied asylum-seeking child is a child who is claiming asylum in their own right (Department for Education, 2017), who is separated from both parents, and who is not currently being cared for by an adult who in law or by custom has the responsibility to do so.

Unaccompanied asylum-seeking children are defined as both unaccompanied asylum-seeking children and unaccompanied refugee children, who are looked after children and young people (Meredew and Sampeys, 2015).

Albania, Afghanistan and Eritrea have been the most common countries of origin for these children in recent years; however, due to more recent events, there has been an increase in children fleeing Syria. Wherever the child has come from, the most immediate issue will be communication, and it is essential to establish links with local interpreting services that are culturally and ethnically appropriate for the child's background. The local authority in which the child is placed will be able to identify appropriate interpreting services in the area.

From a legal and humanitarian perspective, it is recognised that children seeking asylum are fleeing war, torture, persecution, threat to life, or political unrest, and the Home Office has a duty to have a regard to the need to safeguard and promote the welfare of these children. Local authorities have a duty to accommodate such children and young people under section 20 of the Children Act 1989, and so they may be placed with foster carers.

It therefore follows that unaccompanied asylum-seeking children will often have complex physical and mental health needs which, due to language, cultural and other barriers, may be delayed in their identification, or may not be present at the time of their initial health assessment. The mental health of these children can also deteriorate as a result of increased stress when applying for asylum, which is a very complex and lengthy process.

It is important that foster carers are vigilant when caring for asylum-seeking children, as emotional trauma, such as post-traumatic stress, can lie dormant and only manifest itself once the child or young person has settled into their placement, and feels safe enough to disclose their history or allow their emotions to surface.

Foster carers need to be mindful of the increased incidence of deteriorating mental health in these children and be aware of early signs of increased stress, which may manifest as:

- lack of sleep or difficulty sleeping;

- erratic eating habits, such as binge-eating or refusing to eat;

- low mood and withdrawal;

- social isolation; and,

- in extreme cases, self-harm.

There is also a risk that because of a possibility of disconnect from their religious or cultural needs, these children and young people can be at increased risk of being radicalised (persuaded into adopting extremist, violent views, often through online contact).

Physical symptoms may also lie dormant and manifest themselves at a later date after a period of incubation, such as night sweats and a persistent cough that may be indicative of tuberculosis (TB). This is diagnosed in a significant number of children and young people who have travelled and lived in cramped and dirty conditions for weeks or perhaps months before arriving in the UK.

The majority of children and young people seeking asylum have initially been cared for in Kent, as this is the nearest local authority to Folkestone and Dover, and many migrants cross from Calais by boat or on trucks to seek asylum in the UK. The health services in Kent have by default become experts when it comes to assessing the health needs of children seeking asylum. Their experience has resulted in audits of common symptoms and issues identified at the initial health assessment stage.

One such audit for unaccompanied asylum-seeking children arriving in Kent led to the following levels of screening and interventions (Kent Public Health Observatory, 2016).

Health need	Kent's experience
Screening for tuberculosis	70% screened
Screening for hepatitis B	100% screened
Poor dental health	43%
Visual disturbance/problem	35%
Immunisations	100% needed full vaccination
Psychological/mental health concerns	41%

The above health needs will inform the direction of the initial health assessments locally, and routinely all asylum-seeking children will require dental and GP registration as well as appointments for dental and vision checks as soon as is reasonable. All should be referred for commencement or completion of the universal immunisation schedule (as it is reasonable to assume that asylum-seeking children will have incomplete or uncertain immunisation status and therefore should be treated accordingly). Blood tests, including blood-borne virus (BBV) screening and TB screening, will be required for many, dependent upon the history given and information available on their entry into care.

In an ideal world, these children and young people should be placed with foster carers who have experience and an acquired understanding of this group of children's complex needs. Experienced carers will have gained confidence in navigating their way through services, including immigration services; however, due to increasing demand and limited foster care resources, it is not beyond the realms of possibility for newly approved foster carers to have asylum-seeking children placed with them. Whilst this may be a daunting prospect initially, remember, there is an experienced team of professionals to be called upon to give advice and support.

Pamphlets on unaccompanied asylum-seeking children

CoramBAAF has published a series of six pamphlets for foster carers who are, or who may be, looking after unaccompanied asylum-seeking children. An introductory pamphlet provides general information about why these children may have come to the UK, what their experiences may have been, and what their needs are once they have arrived. Five country-specific pamphlets provide information on countries where many of these children may originate, and what their lives may have been like, with details of culture, religion, schooling, health, diet, and other information. The countries covered are Afghanistan, Eritrea, Iraq, Sudan, and Vietnam.

For more information, visit: https://corambaaf.org.uk/books/caring-unaccompanied-asylum-seeking-children-and-young-people-full-series.

Safe care and infections

Foster carers need to be aware that they may look after a child who has, or who is suspected of having, a blood-borne virus. Any child may be at a small risk of contracting hepatitis B (HBV), hepatitis C (HCV), or Human Immunodeficiency Virus (HIV) by being born to a mother who is infected with one of these blood-borne viruses. A virus can also be transmitted as a result of intravenous street drug use (blood-to-blood contact or sharing needles), sex working, unprotected sex with an infected partner, occupational injuries, non-sterile body piercing, or non-sterile tattooing.

Newborn babies with an identified risk of hepatitis B will be immunised against hepatitis B from birth. To note: there is no immunisation available for hepatitis C or HIV.

When attending to the basic physical needs of a baby or child with suspected or confirmed HBV, HCV or HIV, foster carers should adhere to the same hygiene principles and practice as outlined in the safer care policy of their fostering service. As a foster carer, you will have been given information about safe caring and this good practice should apply to all the children whom you care for.

The possibility of getting HBV, HCV or HIV from an infected child is minimal. Even if a baby or child has been confirmed as having a blood-borne virus, your care of that child should be no different to that of a child without that risk.

By always following the principles and practice of universal precautions, as outlined below, the risk of cross infection will be significantly reduced for everyone.

- Do not share personal items – such as toothbrushes, razors or tweezers.

- Clean up any blood spillages with hot, soapy water, then wipe surfaces with household bleach, then throw the cloth away.

- Cover cuts with a waterproof plaster until healed.

- Wear gloves for nappy changing – this is only required if blood is noticed in the baby's stools or urine.

- Wear gloves for cleaning up the child's vomit – this is only required if blood is noticed in it.

- If you have eczema or psoriasis on your hands and you have areas of broken skin, wear gloves when changing nappies or cleaning up vomit, even if there is no blood noticed – this is to prevent infection from other germs.

- Dispose of used sanitary protection safely and carefully.

- It is recommended that any linen contaminated with blood should be washed at 90 degrees centigrade. However, please be mindful of the washing instructions on the label as this temperature may damage the clothing/linen.

(www.cdc.gov/infectioncontrol/basics)

Note: Urine, faeces, saliva (spit), sputum (phlegm), tears, sweat, and vomit do not carry a risk of HIV, HBV or HCV infection unless they are contaminated with blood.

It is not possible to catch HBV, HCV or HIV from normal social contact, including kissing, coughing, sneezing, holding hands, sharing bathrooms, toilets, swimming pools, food, cups, cutlery and crockery, etc.

5 Foster carers' health

Whilst the majority of this guide is about promoting the health of looked after children, and your role as a foster carer in supporting looked after children in your care to enjoy and participate in activities and lifestyle choices that will have long-term benefits for health, this chapter is about you the foster carer, and the importance of looking after yourself.

This is important, because fostering children in today's care system is challenging at times, and in order to be successful in the role, foster carers have to be both physically and emotionally healthy and resilient.

Based on what we know about the complexities and challenges that foster carers report in supervision sessions and reviews, we have taken a no-nonsense, commonsense approach to this chapter.

If you take into account that children in the care system have higher levels of unmet physical and emotional health needs than their peers (Department for Education and Department of Health, 2015), then it follows that foster carers have to be physically and emotionally healthy to respond effectively to those needs on a daily basis.

There are some obvious actions and lifestyle choices that all foster carers can make to safeguard and promote their own health:

- Regular exercise: this increases the production of mood-boosting hormones called endorphins. These hormones act as transmitters that combat the effects of stress and enhance our immune systems. Exercise can be whatever fits in with your routine and whatever you enjoy doing. You are more likely to stick with an exercise that you enjoy.

- Healthy eating: this should be a whole family approach. Eating fruit, vegetables, whole grains and healthy protein, and avoiding foods with high levels of saturated fats and sugar, will have long-term health benefits for everyone.

- Weight management: obesity is on the increase in the UK, and if left unchecked can lead to a number of health issues, such as Type 2 diabetes, heart disease, stroke and some cancers.

- Smoking: aim to stop, or reduce by swapping to vaping, which is inhaling and exhaling vapour containing nicotine and flavouring in a vaping device. Vaping should be treated in the same way as cigarette smoking. Implement a smoke-free home.

- Alcohol: this can and should be enjoyed in moderation; however, it should not be used as a coping mechanism to reduce stress levels.

- Time out: between placements or during respite periods, do something that you enjoy doing, such as going on a short holiday or perhaps to a spa for some pampering, as a treat. Even a day or a few hours off to enjoy a hobby can help to revitalise you and recharge your batteries. Remember to be good to yourself – you deserve it!

These behaviours are also good role-modelling behaviours for children: children are influenced on many levels by the adults caring for them. By adopting healthier lifestyle choices for ourselves, we are sending positive messages to the children in our care that investing in physical and emotional health is important for everyone and will have lifelong benefits.

Caring for a child who has experienced abuse and trauma, even for short periods of time, can be detrimental to a carer's emotional and mental health. In some instances, caring for a child who has experienced trauma can trigger memories of a carer's own traumatic childhood experiences, and this can lead to real emotional turmoil. This, in turn, can cause a loss of confidence and feelings of anxiety that, if left unaddressed, may lead to carers becoming withdrawn and possibly depressed. Foster carers can become emotionally unavailable to the children in their care, in order to protect themselves from further distress.

Some carers may feel that they are failing, and that if they share these feelings and anxieties, they will be judged as not being suitable to continue to foster. This is not the case: professionals involved in fostering understand the challenges faced by carers and the impact this can have on their emotional health. When foster carers are open and honest with professionals supervising the placement, support can be put in place to help them to work through their anxieties and, wherever possible, maintain the placement for the child.

Asking for help from your GP is another positive step. It may be that for a period of time a carer will need to be prescribed medication or counselling to help them overcome periods of anxiety and stress that can affect any of us from time to time. By seeking help, a carer has taken the first positive step towards their own recovery.

A final word...

This guide has been written for newly approved foster carers who are starting their journey in this rewarding and vital role. The authors' hope is that this is a starting point for developing and learning about health and its importance in the lives of children and young people in care, and those who are entrusted with providing that care.

We may not be able to prepare the future for our children, but we can at least prepare our children for the future.

(Franklin D Roosevelt, 1941)

References

Adoption UK (2018) *FASD: The hidden epidemic: Chief Executive's blog*, available at: www.adoptionuk.org/Blog/fasd-the-hidden-epidemic

Alderson H, McGovern R, Brown R, Howel D, Becker F, Carr L, Copello A, Fouweather T, Kaner E, McArdle P, McColl E, Shucksmith J, Stele A, London: Vale L and Lingam R (2017) 'Supporting looked after children and care leavers in decreasing drugs, and alcohol (SOLID): protocol for a pilot feasibility randomised controlled trial of interventions to decrease risky substance use M (drugs and alcohol) and improve mental health of looked after children and care leavers aged 12-20 years', *Pilot Feasibility Studies*, 3:25

ASH (2019) *Factsheet: Young People and Smoking*, available at: https://ash.org.uk

Aynsley A, Bradley R, Buchanan L, Burrow N and Bush M (undated) *Childhood Adversity, Substance Misuse and Young People's Mental Health*, Young Minds Expert Briefing, available at: https://youngminds.org.uk/media/1547/ym-addaction-briefing.pdf

Bazalgette L, Rahilly T and Trevelyan G (2015) *Achieving Emotional Wellbeing for Looked After Children: A whole system approach*, London: NSPCC

Better Health Channel (2015) *Alcohol and Teenagers*, available at: www.betterhealth.vic.gov.au

Berk LE (2010) *Development through the Life Span*, London: Pearson

Bond H (2019) *The Foster Carer's Handbook for Parenting Teenagers*: CoramBAAF

Bryan K (2004) 'Prevalence of speech and language difficulties in young offenders', *International Journal of Language and Communication Disorders*, 39, pp391–400

Carter P (2013) *Parenting a Child with Autism Spectrum Disorder*, London: BAAF

Centers for Disease Control & Prevention (2016) *Standard Precautions for all Patient Care*, available at: www.cdc.gov/infectioncontrol/basics/standard-precautions.html

Children's Legal Centre (1985) 'Landmark decision for children's rights', *Childright*, 22, p 11–18 (see for *Gillick v West Norfolk* and Wisbech Area Health Authority and Department of Health and Social Security [1984] Q.B. 58)

Cook S (2017) *Speech and Language Therapist*, Bath and North East Somerset Community Health Service, available at: https://www.rcn.org.uk/get-involved/forums/children-and-young-people-staying-healthy-forum/communities/looked-after-children

CoramBAAF (2018) *Reducing the Risks of Environmental Tobacco Smoke for Children and their Carers*, Practice Note 68, London: CoramBAAF

Department for Education (2010) *Care Planning, Placement & Case Review (England) Regulations*, London: DfE

Department for Education (2011) *The Fostering Services: National Minimum Standards*, available at: https://assets.publishing.service.gov.uk/government/uploads/system/uploads/attachment_data/file/192705/NMS_Fostering_Services.pdf

Department for Education (2015) *The Children Act 1989: Guidance and regulations Volume 2: Care planning, placement and case review*, available at: https://assets.publishing.service.gov.uk/government/uploads/system/uploads/attachment_data/file/441643/Childr)en_Act_Guidance_2015.pdf

Department for Education (2017) *Care of Unaccompanied Migrant Children and Child Victims of Modern Slavery: Statutory guidance for local authorities*, London: DfE

Department for Education (2019a) *A Guide to Looked After Children Statistics in England*, version 1.4, London, DfE

Department for Education (2019b) *Children Looked after in England (Including Adoption) Year Ending 31st March 2019*, available at: www.gov.uk/government/collections/statistics-looked-after-children

Department for Education (2019c) *Outcomes for children looked after by LAs: 31 March 2018: National statistics*, available at: www.gov.uk/government/collections/statistics-looked-after-children

Department for Education and Department of Health (2015) *Promoting the Health and Well-Being of Looked After Children: Statutory guidance for local authorities, clinical commissioning groups and NHS England*, available at: www.gov.uk/government/publications/promoting-the-health-and-wellbeing-of-looked-after-children--2

Department of Children, Schools and Families and Department of Health (2009) *Promoting the Health and Well-being of Looked after Children*, London: DCSF and DH

Department of Health (2011a) *Physical Activity for Children or Young People (5-18)*, available at: www.gov.uk/government/publications/uk-physical-activity-guidelines

Department of Health (2011b) *Physical Activity for Early Years (under 5's)*, available at: www.gov.uk/government/publications/uk-physical-activity-guidelines

Fenton K (2019) *Parenting a Child with Toileting Issues*, London: CoramBAAF

Forrester D (2012) *Parenting a Child Affected by Parental Substance Misuse*, London: BAAF

Fursland E (2017) *Caring for a Child who has been Sexually Exploited*, London: CoramBAAF

Fursland E (2020) *Caring for Unaccompanied Asylum-Seeking Children and Young People*, London: CoramBAAF (series of six pamphlets)

Goodman R (1997) 'The Strengths and Difficulties Questionnaire: a research note', *Journal of Child Psychology & Psychiatry*, 38

Hughes D (2012) *Parenting a Child with Emotional and Behavioural Difficulties*, London: BAAF

Jackson C (2012) *Parenting a Child with Mental Health Issues*, London: BAAF

Kent Public Health Observatory (2016) *Health Needs Assessment – Unaccompanied children seeking asylum March 2016*, available at: www.kpho.org.uk/__data/assets/pdf_file/0011/58088/Unaccompanied-children-HNA.pdf

Law J, McBean K and Rush R (2011) 'Communication skills in a population of primary school-aged children raised in an area of pronounced social disadvantage', *International Journal of Language and Communication Disorders*, 46:6, pp 657–664

Mather M (2018) *Dealing with Foetal Alcohol Spectrum Disorder*, London: CoramBAAF

Meredew F and Sampeys C (2015) *Promoting the Health of Children in Public Care*, London: BAAF

National Childhood Measurement Programme (2013), available at: www.gov.uk/government/collections/national-child-measurement-programme

NHS England (2019) *Personalised Care*, available at: www.england.nhs.uk/personalisedcare

NICE (2014) *Interventions to Reduce Substance Misuse among Vulnerable Young People*, Evidence Update 56, London: NICE

Nixon C, Elliott L and Henderson M (2019) 'Providing sex and relationships education for looked after children: a qualitative exploration of how personal and institutional factors promote or limit the experience of role ambiguity, conflict and overload among caregivers', *British Medical Journal Online*, 9:4

Patton GC, Selzer R, Coffey C, Carlin JB and Wolfe R (1999) 'Onset of adolescent eating disorders: population based cohort study over three years', *British Medical Journal*, 318, pp 765–768

Phillips R (2004) *Children Exposed to Parental Substance Misuse*, London: BAAF

Popova S (2017) 'Counting the cost of drinking alcohol during pregnancy', *Bulletin of the World Health Organization*, 95:5, pp. 313–388

Prison Reform Trust (2016) *In Care, Out of Trouble: How the life chances of children in care can be transformed by protecting them from unnecessary involvement in the criminal justice system*, available at: www.prisonreformtrust.org.uk/Portals/0/Documents/In%20care%20out%20of%20trouble%20summary.pdf

Public Health England (2018) *Best Start in Life and Beyond: Improving public health outcomes for children, young people and families: Guidance to support the commissioning of the Healthy Child Programme 0–19: Health visitor and school nurse commissioning*, available at: www.gov.uk/government/

publications/healthy-child-programme-0-to-19-health-visitor-and-school-nurse-commissioning

Public Health England and Department of Health (2017) *Immunisations against Infectious Disease*, available at: www.gov.uk/government/collections/immunisation-against-infectious-disease-the-green-book

Scottish Government (2014) *Guidance on Health Assessments for Looked After Children in Scotland*, Edinburgh: Scottish Government

Sheridan M, Sharma A and Cockerill H (2014) *Mary Sheridan's From Birth to Five Years* (4th edn), London: Routledge

Tarren-Sweeney M (2011) 'Concordance of mental health impairment and service utilisation among children in care', *Clinical Child Psychology and Psychiatry*, 15:4, pp 481–495

Welsh Assembly Government (2007) *Towards a Stable Life and a Brighter Future*, Cardiff: Welsh Assembly Government

Wheeler R (2006) 'Gillick or Fraser? A plea for consistency over competence in children: Gillick and Fraser are not interchangeable', *British Medical Journal*, 332:7545, p 807

Useful resources

The Eatwell Guide
A tool that defines Government recommendations on eating healthily and achieving a balanced diet for adults and children.

www.gov.uk/government/publications/the-eatwell-guide

Caroline Walker Trust
This organisation is dedicated to the improvement of public health through good food. A major part of their work is to produce expert reports that establish nutritional guidelines for vulnerable groups – including children and older people.

www.cwt.org.uk/

British Heart Foundation
Provides information about staying fit and active as a family for a heart-healthy lifestyle.

www.bhf.org.uk/informationsupport/support/healthy-living/staying-active/staying-active-as-a-family

Change 4 Life
Provides information about healthy lifestyles for families.

www.nhs.uk/change4life

Public Health England[1]
Provides English and maths teaching resources and whole-school materials that support teachers to educate pupils about how much sugar is in their

---

1   At the time of publication, the Minister for Health in England confirmed plans to abolish Public Health England in favour of a new agency that will specifically deal with protecting the country from pandemics; this was in response to the coronavirus pandemic of 2020. This is unlikely to affect the local government arrangements for public health services, and advice and information will continue to be available on local authority websites.

everyday food and drink, and to empower them and their families to make healthier choices.

www.campaignresources.phe.gov.uk/schools/topics/healthy-eating/overview

NHS UK

This is a helpful source (previously known as NHS Choices) that has information regarding local health services including dentists, GPs, etc. It also has an A-Z information page on heath conditions and treatments.

www.nhs.uk/

Health for Teens

This is an excellent website for adolescents, with lots of information regarding sexual health, relationships, lifestyle, drugs, etc.

www.healthforteens.co.uk/

Young Minds

Provides mental health and well-being information for children and young people, and also information for professionals.

www.youngminds.org.uk

Frank

Provides useful information on drugs for children, young people and adults.

www.talktofrank.com

Drug Education Forum

A forum of national organisations committed to improving the practice and profile of drug education in England.

www.drugeducationforum.com/

Drink Aware

Advice, tips and facts about alcohol and underage drinking.

www.drinkaware.co.uk/advice/underage-drinking/

Gillick competency and Fraser guidelines

The Gillick competency and Fraser guidelines help people who work with children to balance the need to listen to children's wishes with the responsibility to keep them safe.

https://learning.nspcc.org.uk/media/1541/gillick-competency-factsheet.pdf